D1008538

WITHIN THY HAND

My Poem Book of Prayers

WITHIN THY HAND

My Poem Book of Prayers

by ILO ORLEANS

Illustrated by SIEGMUND FORST

UNION OF AMERICAN HEBREW CONGREGATIONS
New York

To GOLDA and LEAH
dear and
devoted sisters

Library of Congress Catalogue Card Number: 61-15353

Poems: Copyright, 1961 by
ILO ORLEANS

Illustrations: Copyright, 1961 by
UNION OF AMERICAN HEBREW CONGREGATIONS
NEW YORK

PRINTED IN U.S. OF AMERICA

Editor's Introduction

All prayer is poetry. Then why write new poems from old prayers? Because every prayer has at its heart an experience which cannot fully be expressed even in the clear and classic words generations have come to love and cherish. The worshipper must always fill out the poetry of the prayer with the artistry of his soul.

The modern child knows the experience which seeks expression in prayer but the words of the prayer book often seem distant from his own fresh emotions. Yet his people has found its own experience enriched and refined by the words which the prior generations of Israel have bequeathed as guide and goal to its children.

To know the meaning of Israel's heartfelt prayer is to express it in a way the modern child can understand, thus to stand as a bridge between the praying generations. This is the poet's task as he translates the Siddur into modern verse. Praised be He who has given His people this blessed heritage and those who renew it in each generation.

RABBI EUGENE B. BOROWITZ
Director of Education

By Way of Preface

This little sheaf of poems is intended to serve as a pleasant gateway for young people to the formal book of prayer. An effort has here been made to grasp and preserve the spirit, the flavor, the essence and, indeed, some of the phraseology, of the traditional, historic prayers, upon which these poems are based.

By the rhymes and rhythms which have been employed, I have sought a method by which the young — and the old as well — could learn to strengthen and sustain their interest in, and their love for, the notable words of faith in our heritage. One who strives to be a poet will surely be forgiven for his conviction that the basic and underlying thoughts, inherent in prayer, may be provided more readily, meaningfully, and effectively by poetry than by prose.

Since prayer represents the unceasing urge for strengthening the link between the human and the Divine, between the finite and the Infinite, between the mortal and the Eternal, there will remain, from generation to generation, a constant quest for richness in the expression and in the presentation of words of prayer, as they reach out from man to God!

These poems represent a phase of this spiritual search. It is my hope that by utilization of these prayer-poems a firm foundation may be laid in the religious instruction of our youth, upon which spiritual understanding can grow, in beauty, in worth, and in strength!

ILO ORLEANS

Acknowledgments

Appreciative indebtedness is acknowledged by me to Dr. Eugene B. Borowitz for his friendly, painstaking editorial guidance; to Dr. Samuel White Patterson, Professor Emeritus of Hunter College, Rabbis Solomon B. Freehof and Herbert Weiner, and Dr. Emanuel Gamoran for their inspiration and their valued comments; to Rabbis Leon Kronish, Samuel H. Markowitz, and Paul M. Steinberg for their appraisal of the text; to Ralph Davis for his characteristically fine format in designing this volume; to Professor Philip Gordon, of Princeton, N. J., friend of a lifetime, for the music with which he has shed luster upon hundreds of my poems, including some in the present compilation; to my secretary, Ann Cahn, and to Julia Minor and Sylvia Schiff for their cooperation in a multiplicity of details essential for the metamorphosis from manuscript to book.

A special word of gratitude I must express to my dedicated wife, Friede, for her encouragement and unfailing helpfulness.

Choral settings have been fashioned for the following poems, which have been issued as sheet music, copyrighted, and published as here indicated:

By Remick Music Corporation (Music by Philip Gordon):

   God of Mercy and Peace © 1957
   Let the Earth Be Glad © 1961
   Within Thy Light © 1961

By G. Schirmer, Inc. (Music by Philip Gordon):
   Evening Prayer © 1956

By Summy-Birchard Co.:

   My Rock, My Fortress (Music by Philip Gordon)
     © 1955 (Poem listed as My Strength! My Song! page 17)

   I Lift My Eyes (Music by Lloyd Pfautsch) © 1955

ILO ORLEANS

The Poems

Within Thy Hand

בְּיָדְךָ אַפְקִיד רוּחִי׃

Within Thy hand,
O gracious God,
My soul, my spirit I entrust.
Ay, Thou hast cleansed
And freed me, Lord;
For Thou art true and right and just.

Thanks, O Lord

מוֹדֶה אֲנִי

Thanks, O Lord,
To Thee, I give —
  God of all
  Who breathe and live,

Who wakest me
With light of day,
  That I, refreshed,
  May walk Thy way.

Thanks, O Lord,
I give to Thee,
  Lord of earth
  And sky and sea,

Who leadest me,
With loving care,
  To know Thy blessings
  Everywhere.

3

The Happy Man

אַשְׁרֵי הָאִישׁ

Happy the man
Who walks erect
And turns from dark and evil ways,
Who will not sit
With those who scorn,
But seeks the Lord, and hymns His praise.

In God's eternal
Truths he finds
His strength and comfort and delight —
And meditates
With heart and soul
On Heaven's laws, by day and night.

And he shall flourish
Like a tree,
Planted by a running stream,
That grows and leafs
And spreads and fruits,
Radiant in sunlight gleam.

The righteous man
Shall stride through life,
Steadfast, sturdy, strong, and true —
And he shall prosper
All his days
In all the work that he shall do.

Not so the way
Of wicked men —
But like the chaff that has no worth —
Tossed and driven
By the winds —
They shall perish from the earth.

The Heavens Declare

הַשָּׁמַיִם מְסַפְּרִים כְּבוֹד אֵל

The Heavens declare
　　The grandeur of God —
The stars in their courses
　　Sing out the Lord's name.

The wonders of earth,
　　And the seas and the skies,
By night and by day,
　　His glory proclaim.

The Lord Shall Reign
Forever More

יִמְלֹךְ יִמְלֹךְ יְיָ יִמְלֹךְ לְעֹלָם וָעֶד׃

The kingdom of
The Lord extends
   Beyond creation's
   Furthest shore.

The Lord doth reign;
The Lord hath reigned;
   The Lord shall reign
   Forever more.

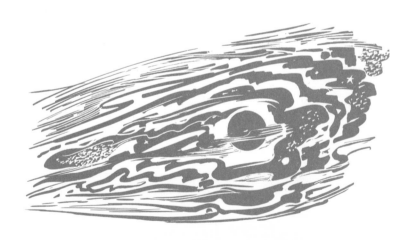

Hear, O Israel

שְׁמַע יִשְׂרָאֵל
יְהֹוָה אֱלֹהֵינוּ יְהֹוָה אֶחָד׃

Hear, O hear,
O Israel;
    The Lord, our God,
    Is ONE.

Blessed, blessed
Be His name,
    Whose Will is
    Ever done.

Love the Lord!

וְאָהַבְתָּ אֵת יְיָ אֱלֹהֶיךָ:

And you shall love
The Lord, your God,
    With all your heart
    And soul and might.

And may these words,
Within your heart,
    Forever be
    A shining light.

Unto your children
Teach these words;
    Instruct them well
    To understand

The meaning of
These things which I,
    The Lord, your God,
    Today command.

And speak of them
Within your home;
    When you are walking
    By the way;

And speak of them
When you arise,
    And when you rest
    At close of day.

And bind them as
A sign of faith
    Upon your head,
    And on your hand —

And write them down
Within your house,
    On gates and doorposts
    Through the land!

Bless the Lord

בָּרְכוּ

Come, bless the Lord,
The Lord of all,
Whose name forever shall be blest.

We bless Thee, Lord,
And through our days
Thy light and love shall be our quest.

True Is God's Word

True and faithful,
And sound
Is Thy word;
Beautiful, pleasant,
And sweet
To be heard.

Thy Word is beloved,
And constant,
And right;
To all of Thy children
Thy word
Brings delight.

Revered and honored,
And good,
And pure,
Forever and ever
Thy word
Shall endure.

Rock of Israel

צוּר יִשְׂרָאֵל

God, mighty Rock
Of Israel,
Whose holy name is ever blessed —

Arise, O Lord,
Grant help to all
The persecuted and oppressed.

Evening Prayer

הַשְׁכִּיבֵנוּ

Let us, O Lord,
Lie down in peace;
    And let us rise
    To love of life.

Spread the mantle
Of Thy grace;
    Guard us, God,
    From storms of strife.

Direct our feet,
So we may walk
    The roadway bright
    With Heaven's flame;

And save us, Lord,
So we may live
    To bless and praise
    Thy holy name.

Be unto us
A protecting shield,
    To ward off famine,
    Plague, and sword;

And keep from us
Our enemies,
    All evil, and
    All grief, O Lord.

God of compassion,
Shelter us,
    Grant us refuge
    'Neath Thy wing,

Our Guardian,
Our Deliverer,
    O merciful
    And gracious King.

My Strength! My Song!

עָזִּי וְזִמְרָת יָהּ :

My rock, my fortress,
    My strength, my rod,
My shield, my shelter
    Art Thou, Lord God!

My help, my refuge,
    My staff, my light,
May I find favor
    In Thy sight.

My Lord, Thou art
    My hope, my song.
Be Thou my guide
    My whole life long.

By Night and Day

בָּרוּךְ יְיָ בַּיּוֹם, בָּרוּךְ יְיָ בַּלָּיְלָה׃

Blessed be
The Lord by day.

Blessed be
The Lord by night.

Blessed be
The Lord by night.

Blessed be
The Lord by day.

Blessed be
The Lord who grants

Blessed be
The Lord who gives

Us restful sleep
Till morning light.

The will to live,
To work, to pray.

God of Mercy and Peace

מְכַלְכֵּל חַיִּים

God of Mercy and Peace,
   Who sustainest the living,
To Thee, all who breathe
   Sing psalms of thanksgiving.

Thou feedest the hungry;
   Thou leadest the blind;
Thou, Rock of the Ages
   For all of mankind.

Thou healest the sick;
   Raisest up those who fall;
Givest heart to the weary;
   Thou, Guardian of all.

Thou clothest the naked,
   Thou loosest the bound;
In Thee, God, alone
   Salvation is found.

Grant Thou Peace, O Lord

שִׂים שָׁלוֹם

Bring, O Lord,
The joy of peace;
　　Cause the light
　　Of Heaven's face
To shine on men
Throughout the earth;
　　And bless them with
　　Thy love and grace.

For, Thou hast taught
The law of life.
　　Within our hearts
　　Thou didst instil
The ways of truth
And righteousness,
　　That we may learn
　　To do Thy will.

And always, in
Thy holy sight,
　　Heaven's favor
　　May we find.
Abundant peace
Grant Thou, O Lord —
　　Peace to brighten
　　All mankind.

21

Thou Knowest, Lord

אַתָּה יוֹדֵעַ רָזֵי עוֹלָם

Thou knowest, Lord,
The secrets of
Thy infinite creation —
Of endless space
And time, which stretch
Beyond imagination.

The mysteries
Of life and death
And all eternity
Bewilder man,
But naught is veiled,
O Lord, our God, from Thee.

And Thou dost search
The inner depths
Of head and heart and soul.
All things are clear
And plainly writ
On Thy eternal scroll.

I Lift My Eyes

אֶשָּׂא עֵינַי אֶל־הֶהָרִים

Unto the hills
    I lift my eyes,
And see their splendor
    Reach the skies.

"Whence comes to me
    My help?" I cry.
My help is from
    The Lord on high,

Who fashioned heaven
    And land and sea
And rules for all
    Eternity.

The Upright Man

יְהֹוָה מִי-יָגוּר בְּאׇהֳלֶךָ:

O Lord, within
Thy Tabernacle,
Who shall make his dwelling place?
And high upon
Thy holy mountain
Who shall see Thee face to face?

The upright man
Who, all his days,
From faith in Thee will not depart —
Whose works are works
Of righteousness,
Who speaks the truth within his heart;

Upon whose tongue
No slander lies —
Who, mindful of a man's good name,
Will never bring
His neighbor harm —
Nor bear the guilt of spreading shame —

Who honors those
Who fear the Lord,
For they find favor in his eyes;
But men of power,
Wealth or fame,
If they be vile, he does despise;

Whose lips will never
Falsely speak —
Although to his own hurt he swears;
Who lends, with grace
A helping hand —
For Honor is the badge he wears;

Within whose soul
The light of love,
Of God, and man, shall ever burn.
The pure and perfect
Man, in Thine
Abode eternal shall sojourn.

The Judgments of the Lord Are Just

תּוֹרַת יְיָ תְּמִימָה:

How *perfect* is
The law of God,
Where joy for the spirit lies.
Sure are the teachings
Of the Lord,
Which make the simple wise.

Righteous are
The rules of God,
Rejoicing the human heart.
Pure are all
Of God's commands —
The Lord's unchanging chart!

Clean is the fear,
The love of God —
The Lord's eternal light.
The judgments of
The Lord are *just* —
Forever true and right.

26

Teach Me, Lord

הוֹרֵנִי יְהֹוָה דֶּרֶךְ חֻקֶּיךָ׃

Teach me, Lord,
    To know Thy ways —
To walk therein
    Throughout my days.

With Thy gentle
    Guiding hand,
Teach me, Lord,
    To understand,

Grant me favor
    In Thy sight,
And by the lamp
    Of Heaven's light,

And hold in love,
    Respect, and awe,
Thy precepts and
    Thy holy law —

In Thy pathways
    Make me tread,
Pure in heart
    And soul and head.

That I may never
    Cease to bless
Thy mercy and
    Thy righteousness.

Blessing for the Torah

אֲשֶׁר נָתַן לָנוּ תּוֹרַת אֱמֶת:

Be blessed, O Lord,
Who fashioned man
In image that is like to Thine,
And in whose soul
Thou didst implant
The sacred spark which is Divine;

Who gavest us,
By Moses' hand,
Thy everlasting holy Word,
Of justice and
Of righteousness,
Which Israel at Sinai heard.

Blessed be Thou,
Eternal God,
Lord of Lords, and King of Kings,
The fount of truth,
Whose ageless law
Is tree of life to which man clings.

Let the Earth Be Glad

יִשְׂמְחוּ הַשָּׁמַיִם וְתָגֵל הָאָרֶץ

Let the Earth be glad.
Let the Heavens above
Rejoice and smile and sing;
Among the nations,
Let them say:
"God reigns. The Lord is King!"

Let the oceans roar,
With their teeming life.
Let the spreading golden plains
And the mighty trees
Of the forest shout:
"The Lord is King! God reigns!"

Give thanks to God,
For He is good;
His blessings are descending,
Like cleansing rain
Throughout the earth,
With love that is unending.

Blessing for the Haftorah

אֲשֶׁר בָּחַר בִּנְבִיאִים טוֹבִים

Blessed art Thou,
    Our Lord sublime,
Whose reign extends
    Beyond all time,

Whose prophets preached,
    When mankind erred,
And taught Thy truth —
    Thy Holy Word.

Blessed art Thou,
    Our God, our King —
Gladden our hearts
    That we may sing

Of Sabbath joy,
    Thy law we bless,
Of Thee, and of
    Thy holiness.

And be Thou blessed,
    Our Shield, our Rod,
Our mighty Rock,
    O Lord, our God.

30

Tree of Life

עֵץ חַיִּים

A tree of Life
Is the Word of God
To all who seek its strength;

And those who tend
And cherish it
Shall be enriched, at length.

Its wisdom and
Enduring truth
Make joy of life increase.

Its ways are ways
Of sweet content —
And all its paths are peace!

Adoration

עָלֵינוּ

It is our duty,
It is our joy,
To praise the King of Kings,
The God of all
The universe —
The Master of all things;

Who fashioned man
With spark divine —
And, by His will, did bless
The human heart
To understand
The ways of godliness.

We know that God
Is ONE alone —
The King of all creation.
To Him, for all
Of endless time,
Man bows in adoration.

O What Is Man?

מָה אֱנוֹשׁ כִּי־תִזְכְּרֶנּוּ

O what is man,
That Thou dost give
Thy thought to him on Earth?
Or the son of man,
That Thou dost mark
His life, his death, his birth?

Yet, in Thine image,
By Thy word,
Was man made like to Thee;
And Thou, O Lord,
Hast fashioned him
With immortality.

With honor and
With glory, Lord,
Has man, by Thee, been crowned.
Thou gavest man
Dominion o'er
Thy creatures all around.

All fowl, all fish,
All beasts that breathe,
In air and sea and field,
By Thy command,
To man must bend,
And to man's will must yield.

How mighty and
How wondrous are
The works that Thou hast made;
And Thou dost grant
To man, O Lord,
Thy bounty and Thy aid.

Kaddish

קַדִּישׁ

We sanctify
The name of God.
Our lips His praises shall repeat.
His majesty
We shall proclaim
In hour of sorrow or defeat.

God's justice and
His truth endure.
What mortal mind is there who can
Perceive the mystic
Ways of God —
Whose hand made Heaven, Earth, and man?

The kingdom of
The Lord shall spread
Its glory till all time shall cease;
And in the hearts
Of men shall reign
The blessedness and joy of peace.

Our God

(En Kelohenu)

אֵין כֵּאלֹהֵינוּ

None, O none
    Is like our God.
None, O none
    Is like our Lord.
None, O none
    Is like our King.
None is like
    Our Saviour.

Who is like
    Unto our God?
Who is like
    Unto our Lord?
Who is like
    Unto our King?
Who is like
    Our Saviour?

Thanks we give
    Unto our God.
Thanks we give
    Unto our Lord.

Thanks we give
    Unto our King;
And thanks unto
    Our Saviour.

Blessed, blessed
    Is our God.
Blessed, blessed
    Is our Lord.
Blessed, blessed
    Is our King.
And blessed is
    Our Saviour.

Thou art our God —
    Our God Thou art.
Thou art our Lord —
    Our Lord Thou art.
Thou art our King —
    Our King Thou art.
Thou art, Thou art
    Our Saviour.

Benediction

יְבָרֶכְךָ יְיָ וְיִשְׁמְרֶךָ:

May the Father
Of all men
Bless thee, child, and watch o'er thee.
May the love
Of Heaven shine
And kindle faith and bravery.

May the Lord,
All-merciful,
Lift His countenance to thine,
Protect thee from
All harm, my child,
And unto thee grant peace Divine!

39

Behold, How Pleasant

הִנֵּה מַה-טּוֹב וּמַה נָּעִים

Behold, how pleasant,
    And how good,
For men to dwell
    In brotherhood;

When envy, greed,
    And hatred cease,
And men can walk
    The paths of peace.

The Heavens smile
    When men agree,
And work, as friends,
    In harmony.

The Blessed Life

אַשְׁרֶיךָ וְטוֹב לָךְ:

How blessed is
The man who sees
    The labor of
    His hand and head
Yield to him
Its full reward —
    That he may eat
    His daily bread.

How blessed is
The man who finds
    That with his lot
    He is content —
Who works and strives
And builds and dreams
    And reaps a harvest
    Heaven-sent.

O Lord Eternal

אֲדֹנָי מָעוֹן אַתָּה הָיִיתָ לָּנוּ בְּדוֹר וָדוֹר׃

O Lord Eternal,
 God of Grace,
Who rulest through
 All time and space;

Thou, Everlasting
 Lord, didst see
The dawn of all
 Eternity;

And when the endless
 Years roll by,
Thou still shalt reign
 And rule on high.

A thousand years
 Within Thy sight
Are but a hurried
 Watch by night.

Yet, Thou observest
 Man on earth,
Quickened by spark
 Of Thee, at birth;

And though a fleeting
 Passing shade,
From him Thy mercy
 Shall not fade.

Ay, numbered are
 Our days, we know —
For men are born
 To die, and go —

Like shadows in
 The night they pass —
Their years are like
 The withered grass.

O grant us wisdom,
    God, that we
May yearn to live
    With joy in Thee.

O grant us faith,
    That we may find
Thy light, in soul
    And heart and mind.

O grant us guidance,
    Lord, until
Our hands shall work
    To do Thy will.

Within Thy vineyard,
    Teach us, Lord,
The arts of peace —
    And not the sword.

O grant us strength
    To live our years
Secure in Thee,
    And free from fears;

And through our span
    Of earthly days,
To walk Thy paths
    And hymn Thy praise!

Blessing for Bread

הַמּוֹצִיא לֶחֶם מִן הָאָרֶץ׃

Blessed be Thou,
    O Lord, our King,
Creator of every
    Living thing —

Master of all
    The world around,
Who bringest bread
    Out of the ground.

Prayer for Happy Times

שֶׁהֶחֱיָנוּ

Blessed is God,
Our Lord, our King,
    Whose mighty laws
    All worlds obey —

Who gave us life,
Who gave us health,
    Who gave us strength
    To reach this day.

45

Grace After Meals

הַזָּן אֶת הַכֹּל׃

Blessed art Thou,
    O Lord, our King,
Who feedest every
    Living thing;

Who givest bread,
    So that we may
Have strength to do
    Our work each day;

Who dost sustain,
    With loving care,
All Thy creatures
    Everywhere.

Blessed art Thou,
    For Thou dost give
Food to nourish
    All that live.

47

Ever-Righteous Is the Lord

טוֹב לְהֹדוֹת

How good it is
To give my thanks,
    And sing, O Lord,
    My praise of Thee.

Thy mercy and
Thy faithfulness
    Are everywhere
    For eyes to see.

Thy works bring gladness
To my heart;
    And I shall triumph
    In Thy hand.

From day to day
Thy wonders spread,
    Which all — but fools —
    Can understand.

Although the wicked
Seem to thrive —
    As beasts they perish
    From the earth.

For just and righteous
Is the Lord —
    Sustaining all
    Who know His worth.

The righteous flourish
Like the palms.
    Their lives are blessed.
    Their days are long;

And like the cedars
Of Lebanon
    They shall stand
    Secure and strong.

And ever shall
The righteous be
    The witness to
    His righteousness.

The labors and
The lives of all
    Whose hearts are pure,
    The Lord shall bless.

Kiddush

קִדּוּשׁ

Upon the eve
   Of the seventh day,
We lift the golden
   Cup, and pray

Of constant faith,
   Dear God, in Thee,
Father of all
   Humanity,

Our holy Sabbath —
   Day of rest —
By grace and love
   Of God, be blest.

Who taught all men
   To understand
The worth of work
   With head and hand.

And blessed be
   This cup of wine.
May it be
   A sacred sign

And as our week-day
   Labors cease,
Bring the calm
   Of Sabbath peace.

Fill our Sabbath —
   The whole day long —
With joy and gladness,
   Love and song.

A Woman of Valor

אֵשֶׁת חַיִל

A woman of valor
    Is priceless treasure —
Her worth, her merit
    Beyond all measure.

With pride, her husband
    Knows he must,
Within her heart,
    Place all his trust.

And he shall prosper
    At her side;
In peace and plenty
    They abide.

The earnest, eager,
    Faithful wife
Plans works of goodness
    All her life.

She serves her home.
    With willing hands;
Its needs, its ways
    She understands;

And no reward,
    But this, she asks —
To do, in joy,
    Her daily tasks.

Her household is
    Her heart's delight —
Her happiness
    By day and night.

Her children gain,
    With tender care,
The food they eat,
    The clothes they wear.

The poor and needy
    Ever bless
Her gracious acts
    Of kindliness.

Her children bless her
    And her ways.
With love her husband
    Speaks her praise.

Her eyes look toward
    The days ahead;
Her own will lack
    Nor roof, nor bread.

"Ay, many daughters
    Have builded well,
But all of them
    Thou dost excel."

The words within
    Her mouth are wise;
And on her tongue
    No harshness lies.

Grace is deceitful,
    And beauty vain.
An upright woman
    Doth God sustain.

Her walls reflect
    Her warm caress;
For her, no taste
    Of idleness.

She harvests fruit
    Of her own hand;
And honor is hers
    Throughout the land.

Shout in Joy unto the Lord

הָרִיעוּ לַיְיָ כָּל הָאָרֶץ:

Come, all the Earth,
And shout in joy!
    Unto the Lord
    Give thanks in song.
Come, serve the Lord
Who made us all.
    In God's green pasture
    We belong.

Come, enter now
His holy gates,
    For safe within
    God's fold we rest.
Give thanks to Him,
Within His courts,
    And be His name
    Forever blessed!

Good is the Lord.
For all of time
    His love and mercy
    Shall endure.
From generation
To generation,
    Through faith in God,
    Is man secure!

A New Song Let Us Sing

שִׁירוּ לַיְיָ שִׁיר חָדָשׁ:

A new sweet song
Unto the Lord,
A new song let us sing.
O bless His name;
Let all the earth,
In song, His praises ring.

For great is God.
Come, worship Him.
To Him shall praise be given.
With honor, He
Forever reigns —
Creator of Earth and Heaven.

From day to day
Proclaim His power;
His wondrous works declare,
And speak of God's
Great glory to
All nations everywhere.

Let sea and sky
And earth rejoice.
Be glad, ye fields and trees;
For God will judge
The world with truth
And love, by His decrees.

55

Within Thy Light

בְּאוֹרְךָ נִרְאֶה אוֹר:

Within Thy light
O Lord, our God,
We shall see light — we shall see light —
The light of faith,
The light of peace,
The light of love and truth and right.

Within Thy light,
O Lord of all,
We shall see light — the light that spreads
The warmth and glow
Of brotherhood,
And Heaven's blessings on our heads.

O God of all
The world of worlds,
Where naught is hidden from Thy sight —
Within Thy light —
Thy holy light,
We shall see light — we shall see light.

God's Teaching

אַתָּה חוֹנֵן לְאָדָם דַּעַת:

Thou, God, hast planted
   In mortal mind
The seed of knowledge —
   That man may find

Thou teachest him
   To understand
The way shown by
   Thy outstretched hand,

The beauty and
   The joys of life,
In ways of peace
   Instead of strife.

Distinguishing
   The *wrong* from *right,*
And *work* from *rest,*
   And *dark* from *light.*

Through Thee alone,
   Who art All-Good,
All men shall live
   In Brotherhood!

57

From First to Last

עַל הָרִאשׁוֹנִים וְעַל הָאַחֲרוֹנִים

For ages past,
For future years,
Thy word forever shall endure.

Eternal is
Thy righteous truth —
Sound and steadfast, strong and sure.

Thou, Source of life,
There is none else.
No mortal comprehends Thy powers.

Almighty, Ever-
lasting Lord,
Our fathers' God, Thou art, and ours.

Yom Kippur

יוֹם כִּפּוּר:

Lord of Heaven
    And land and sea,
Who fashioned man
    Like unto Thee,

This day of fasting,
    This day of prayer,
Thy sons and daughters
    Everywhere,

Their errors and
     Their wrongs confess,
And beg for Thy
     Forgiveness.

For length of life,
     For health, we pray
Upon this holiest
     Holy Day!

All merciful,
     All gracious God,
Whose sacred word,
     Or thought, or nod

Makes endless worlds
     Revolve in space,
Upon us cause
     To shine Thy face.

Grant strength to us,
     And light our way,
And bless us, this
     Atonement Day!

Sukos Song

חַג הַסֻּכּוֹת:

It's harvest time,
It's harvest time,
How rich is nature's yield
In fruit of earth
And bush and tree,
From orchard, farm, and field.

It's autumn time,
It's autumn time,
When leaves turn gold and red.
In smiling sky
And land and sea
God's glories are outspread.

It's Sukos time,
It's Sukos time,
This day of our thanksgiving.
We hymn the praise
Of God above
For all the joys of living.

Eight Are the Lights

הַנֵּרוֹת הַלָּלוּ אֲנַחְנוּ מַדְלִיקִין׃

Eight are the lights
    Of Chanuko
We light for a week
    And a day.
We kindle the lights,
    And bless the Lord,
And sing a song,
    And pray.

Eight are the lights
    Of Chanuko
For *justice* and *mercy*
    And *love*,
For *charity, courage*
    And *honor* and *peace*,
And *faith* in Heaven
    Above.

Eight are the lights
    Of Chanuko
To keep ever bright
    Memories
Of the valiant soul
    And the fighting heart
And the hope of the
    Maccabees!

63

Purim

פּוּרִים

Purim Day is a *jolly* day,
    When every Jew rejoices.
Purim Day is a *happy* day
    For laughing hearts and voices.

Purim Day is a *friendly* day,
    A holiday so pleasant,
That everyone is glad to give,
    And glad to get a present.

Purim Day is a *cheery* day,
    For the fun it's always bringing,
With Purim games and Purim plays,
    And Purim dance and singing!

Purim Day is a *stirring* day.
    We read Queen Esther's story —
Of Mordecai and the Persian king
    In all their ancient glory!

Purim Day is a *festive* day,
    A day for celebrating
Haman's fall — the tyrant, whom
    We never shall stop hating.

Purim Day is a *jolly* day,
    When every Jew rejoices.
Purim Day is a *happy* day
    For laughing hearts and voices.

Old Haggadah

הַגָּדָה שֶׁל פֶּסַח:

It's an old, old book;
    It stands on the shelf.
I know that I cannot
    Read it myself.

But I like to hear
    About this book,
Which is called HAGGADAH.
    I eagerly look

At the yellowing leaves,
    And the deep brown stains,
While grandpa holds me
    Close, and explains

How drops of wine,
    Through year after year,
Had spattered the pages,
    Now, there — and now, here,

From the Kiddush cup
	In an aging hand,
As the wine was blessed
	In a far-off land.

If the old Haggadah
	Had eyes and ears,
It could tell of the Seders
	Of years and years.

From grandpa's grandpa
	This old book came.
He read from it
	By a candle flame.

And now, with eyes
	Of wonder, I look
At great-great-grandfather's
	Passover book!

I Thank You, God

נוֹדֶה לְךָ׃

I thank you, God,
    For so many things —
For the glow and warmth
    That *Sabbath* brings —

For *Tu Bi-Sh'vot* —
    Tree planting day,
For *shalach monos* —
    And *Purim* play —

For *Chanuko's*
    Menorah light —
Haggadah songs
    On *Pesach* night—

For the holy words
    With which we pray —
For the lamp of *Torah*
    Which lights our way.

For *Rosh Ha-shono*
> And the *shofor's* blast;
For tales of honor
> Of Israel's past;

For the stir of pride —
> And the thrill and the glory
That I am a part
> Of the Jewish story!

Appendix

The following references are to the original Biblical texts containing the themes upon which the poetic paraphrases in this book are based.

Many of the traditional Hebraic prayers in the liturgy are included in the *Union Prayerbook* (Revised Edition, 1959), where they may be found, in whole or in part, in Volumes I or II, at the pages indicated in parentheses. Others will be found in the traditional books of prayer.

Biblical Source
(Union Prayerbook reference in parentheses)

PAGE

1	Psalm 31 (cf. I, 99)
5	Psalm 1
7	Psalm 19 (II, 183)
8	(I, 254)
9	Deut. 6:4 (I, 30)
10	Deut. 6:5-9 (I, 30)
11	Num. 6:24-26 (I, 29)
12	(I, 120)
13	(I, 125)
15	(I, 57)
17	Isaiah 12:2 (I, 251)
18	(I, 168)
19	(I, 33)
21	(I, 243)
22	(II, 149)
23	Psalm 121 (II, 7)
24	Psalm 15 (cf. I, 144)
26	Psalm 19 (I, 149)
27	Psalm 119 — Hé (cf. I, 12)
28	(I, 145)
29	I Chron. 16:8-36 (I, 339)
30	(I, 146)
31	Prov. 3:17-18 (I, 150)

PAGE

32	(I, 150)
34	Psalm 8 (II, 306)
36	(I, 77)
38	(I, 155)
39	Num. 6:24-26 (I, 262)
40	Psalm 133 (I, 96)
41	Psalm 128
42	Psalm 90
44	(I, 377)
45	(I, 209)
47	(I, 382)
48	Psalm 92 (I, 8-9)
50	(I, 93)
52	Prov. 31:10-31 (I, 376)
54	Psalm 100 (I, 210)
55	Psalm 96 (I, 48-49)
56	Psalm 36 (I, 352)
57	(I, 297)
58	(cf. I, 123)
60	(cf. II, 170)
62	(cf. I, 212)
63	(cf. I, 91)
64	(cf. I, 298)